JAMES MARSH

BIZARRE BIRDS
& BEASTS

PAVILION

DAWN CHORUS

Imagine birds at break of day
Poised like a band about to play
A bird with beak shaped like a spoon
Stirs to make the morning tune
The hummingbird then draws its bow
To make a noise that's soft and low,
While those that blow or pluck or hoot
Sound like a sax or lyre or flute.
How do creatures calm and gentle
Make a sound so instrumental?

James Marsh

MONKEY PUZZLE

Funny monkey looking cute,
Dressed up in a flying suit –
Goggles for his eyes and nose
Leather trousers to his toes.
Even though his brain is clever
Monkey's puzzled by the leather
To me it seems an awful shame,
I don't know what we hope to gain –
It really does take some explaining,
Why do we put them through such training?

CRAFTY CATS

Cats are crafty, cats are wise,
Cats can even use disguise –
Though sometimes they may look absurd
Just to fool the smallest bird.

Cats are crafty, cats are cruel,
Cats don't live by human rule –
Hunting in and out of house
To tease or scare each little mouse.

THE PELICAN'S BEAK

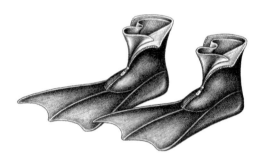

A special beak is the pelican's pride,
It likes to pack its lunch inside.
Scooping fish just like a net,
Why does it let its feet get wet?

Imagine catching all those fish
Without a need for plate or dish.
Or crunching, munching, all day long
Without a moment for a song.

FROG SPURN

A frog in a pond
I am bound to say
Is a friend in every way.
Normally he's kind enough
To be polite and not hop off.

A frog in a pond
I am pleased to say
Is fun to watch at work and play.
If, like me, of frogs you're fond,
Don't be rude and spoil their pond.

SPOT THE LION

The king of beasts is often feared
That in itself is not so weird.
He can get sick like you or me
And then he is a sight to see.

Watch out for this jungle beast
On any mammal he will feast –
And don't forget to take a guide
The lion spots those that do not hide.

Taking this to the very extreme
We all could use some vanishing cream.

FERTLE TURTLE

The turtle is a peculiar bird
Laying 400 eggs, which seems absurd!
It nests in sand, not up a tree
Instead of air it takes to sea.
Turtles fly with flippers spread
Up and down the ocean's bed.

It must be nice to be a turtle,
Especially when you've been so fertle –
I wonder if we'll ever know,
When it flies, where does it go?

TIGER MOTH

Tiger moths are something rare
Seldom seen both here or there.
Not all insects have a sting
They're not out to bug or cling
If you're nervous and you scare
Stop to look or maybe stare.
Moths have got such lovely wings –
Think before you squash the things!

BRIGHT CHAMELEON

A chameleon's skin is most revealing
Changing colour to suit its feeling
If you're an insect on the ceiling
I'll make it clear with whom you're dealing
That tricky tongue could send you reeling.

When a lizard's in this mood
In a temper or a brood
From camouflage it can't be wooed
With these skills we must conclude
It won't end up as someone's food.

THE WISE OWL

Consider this, it's no surprise
The owl is judged as being wise
Sitting still without a sound
Watching everything around
Speaking not a single word
Taking note of what is heard
For knowledge isn't hard to earn –
'The more you listen the more you learn.'

BEAR SKIN

Polar bear sits on a floe
Cosy in his sea of snow
Warm within his coat of fur
With frozen grin he will not stir.

If you want some winter wear
Think twice or thrice before you dare
To choose a fur, and know it's true –
It suits him more than it suits you.

JEWELLED PARROT

I am a jewelled parrot
With bright red ruby eyes
My feathers are of emerald green
I come from paradise.

A golden beak I use to preen
My neck of pearly hue
A priceless gift for any queen –
Don't put me in the zoo.

MOTHER COW

(an udder verse)

The humble cow is also shrewd
Supplying us with creamy food.
She's been around a long, long time,
Through history and nursery rhyme.
Spare a thought for this beast like Venus
When we were babes her milk helped wean us.
And do not take the cow for granted,
Your pints of milk cannot be planted.

FLYING FISH

The flying fish is a very strange dish,
What on earth would we do, if all fish flew?
Holy mackerel! What a place!
Shoals of herring in your face!
You could be resting in the park,
And end up basking with a shark!
Or when it rained, heaven forbid,
Your hair would drip with inky squid!
Imagine seeing when you die,
Your soul skating through the sky,
Perched upon a giant cod,
On its way to meet with God.

FUTURE ARK

Imagine a world where humans would
Do their best for the planet's good:
With water pure and forests fair
No pollution to kill the air.
Can we change our ways much faster
And avoid complete disaster?

Without space to live in peace
The animals will soon decrease
Then disappear without a trace —
Could robot creatures take their place?
There isn't time to wait and see...
The microchip can't make a tree.

To Mum & Dad, the Birds & Bees

First published in Great Britain in 1991 by
PAVILION BOOKS LIMITED
196 Shaftesbury Avenue, London WC2H 8JL

Text and illustrations copyright © James Marsh 1991

Edited, designed and produced by Russell Ash & Bernard Higton

A CIP catalogue record for this book is available
from the British Library

ISBN 1 85145 717 8

1 3 5 7 9 10 8 6 4 2

Printed and bound in Italy by Arnoldo Mondadori